SELECTIONS FROM RIVERDANCE THE SHOW
ARRANGED FOR EASY PIANO

Composed by
BILL WHELAN

Produced by
MOYA DOHERTY

Directed by
JOHN McCOLGAN

Boosey & Hawkes Music Publishers Ltd
www.boosey.com

Published by Boosey & Hawkes Music Publishers Ltd
Aldwych House
71–91 Aldwych
London
WC2B 4HN

www.boosey.com

Copyright © 2014 McGuinness/Whelan Music Publishing Ltd
International copyright secured. All Rights Reserved
Boosey & Hawkes Music Publishers Ltd sole agents

ISMN 979-0-060-12784-7
ISBN 978-0-85162-951-3

First impression 2014

Printed in England by The Halstan Printing Group, Amersham, Bucks

Arrangements for publication by Frank Metis
Original project editor: Peter Pickow
Production photographs by kind permission of Abhann Productions
Cover photography by Hugo Glendinning, Jack Hartin & CJ Mishler

CONTENTS

THE MUSIC OF RIVERDANCE iv

THE HEART'S CRY 2

RIVERDANCE 4

THE COUNTESS CATHLEEN 7

WOMEN OF THE SIDHE 10

SHIVNA 12

THE HARVEST 14

AMERICAN WAKE 16

LIFT THE WINGS 18

HOME AND THE HEARTLAND 21

HEAL THEIR HEARTS 24

MACEDONIAN MORNING 26

OSCAIL AN DORAS 28

Music composed by Bill Whelan
Lyrics by Bill Whelan
Copyright © 1994 McGuinness/Whelan Music Publishing Ltd *except*
Riverdance © 1994 McGuinness/Whelan Music Publishing Ltd and RTÉ Music Ltd

THE MUSIC OF RIVERDANCE

There are two particular problems for the composer writing music in the idiom of any given folk or ethnic tradition - one is social and the other is technical. If the composer is Irish and working with modes and forms of traditional Irish music, then the first of these problems is most acute - and for very positive reasons.

Traditional music holds a special position in Ireland. To many Irish people it has a defining role culturally and provides an authentic and eloquent link to their past. It is also a rich musical vein that reveals much about Ireland and the Irish - quirky, mischievous, evasive dance tunes, and dark proud airs that can heal grief and comfort loss.

From a technical point of view, the instruments from which this music has grown are themselves problematic. In particular the uilleann pipes, not being chromatic, tend to confine melodic writing and the very nature of the instrument itself demands caution. The uilleann pipes are a very beautiful but frustrating combination. Both primitive and sophisticated, their evocative abilities are boundless, but the piper's terror is that they decide to desert him in the midst of his most ardent flight, like some haughty lover - sweet mysterious and unpredictable. This dynamic goes to the heart of piping and the composer may do well to remember the piper's careful pampering of his reeds before setting a note on the page.

Add to this varied demands created by whistles, bodhráns, Irish fiddling styles, and in the case of *Riverdance*, the quirks and vagaries of the Eastern gadulkas and kavals, and soon the relative familiarity of a symphony orchestra may beckon like a safe harbour in a storm.

In such conditions one might never venture out the door. Even ignoring the technical constraints, the social imperatives are daunting enough. However, it is a testament to the robust state of Irish traditional music at this time that there is enough confidence abroad to allow for innovation. While the tradition stands firm, modes of expression are changing and in the broad new church of Irish music, one may now dare to whisper - even to sing.

I have said much about the process of writing for and working with the kinds of musical ingredients that I had chosen for *Riverdance*. However, composition is essentially a solitary occupation, and it is only when you first bring your music into the dance studio that you experience the full rush of fear and excitement. The dancers do not quite know what to expect, and you have no idea how they are going to respond.

It would be folly to suggest that we all knew exactly what we were at, or that there was some kind of grand design. But there is no doubt that as the pieces began to fit together, there was a sense that something unique was happening around and among us. I had deliberately written pieces with rhythmic patterns that were foreign to traditional Irish music, but after the initial raised eyebrows the thrust of the principal dancers' creativity took hold and I can still remember the excitement as they began to fashion their first steps. Gradually these steps were learned by the troupe and I have many memories of arriving to the studio to find individual dancers in corners, corridors and canteens as they worked on the kind of precision that was to become a hallmark of *Riverdance*.

And then came the day that, for me, really copper-fastened it. It was one of the last days of rehearsal for the Eurovision in 1994. Producer Moya Doherty, myself and the entire company were assembled in the dance studio. There was hardly room to move. We had seen the dance performed in sections, but had not seen it all in one piece. The music began, and for the next seven minutes the room was like a power-station. When it was over we all just looked at each other and smiled. There may have been no grand design, but we knew at that moment that whatever it was, it worked. *Riverdance* was truly on its feet and I will never forget it.

I am grateful to the musicians who first played these tunes, and to the various *Riverdance* bands that have performed this music around the world since. Having engaged in similar tasks myself for many years, I am more than aware of the stresses that come with the job. I thank them for their generosity and professionalism, and it is to them that this book is dedicated.

Le mór meas,

Bill Whelan has worked extensively in theatre and film. He was appointed composer to the WB Yeats International Theatre Festival at Ireland's National Abbey Theatre in 1989, writing original music for 15 Yeats plays. His adaptation of *HMS Pinafore* received a Laurence Olivier Award nomination. His compositional work in film includes original scores for *Dancing At Lughnasa* starring Meryl Streep, *Some Mother's Son* starring Helen Mirren and *Lamb* starring Liam Neeson. Music for television includes *The Seven Ages* - Sean Ó Mordha's history of the Irish State.

The Seville Suite was his first large scale orchestral work, commissioned for Ireland's National Day at Expo '92 in Seville. *The Spirit Of Mayo* followed in 1993. *The Connemara Suite*, a trilogy of pieces written for chamber orchestra, premiered in Carnegie Hall in March 2005. The world premiere of the *Riverdance Symphonic Suite*, performed by the RTÉ Concert Orchestra, took place at the National Concert Hall in Dublin in May 2012.

His many production and arranging credits include U2, Van Morrison, Kate Bush, Richard Harris and Planxty. He has written and recorded a new composition with the classical violinist Vanessa-Mae. He has just completed a project with Berklee College of Music in Boston which is being developed into an album.

Bill was honoured with the 1997 Grammy Award for 'Best Musical Show Album' for his *Riverdance* CD. The album is a certified Platinum record in the US, Ireland and Australia. *Riverdance The Show* has been seen live by more than 22 million people and by a television audience of nearly 2 billion.

Bill holds two honorary Doctorates and was awarded a fellowship by the Royal Irish Academy of Music. He is a member of the Boards of Berklee College of Music, The University of Limerick and Ireland's National Music Education Programme - Music Generation, and is adjunct Professor at Trinity College Dublin's School of Drama, Film and Music.

The Heart's Cry

Composed by Bill Whelan · Lyrics by Bill Whelan

Copyright © 1994 McGuinness/Whelan Music Publishing Ltd. International copyright secured. All Rights Reserved.
Boosey & Hawkes Music Publishers Ltd sole agents.

(Solo & Chorus)
dark spring.
fold you.
Warm with a mys - ter - y
I may re - veal to you. In
time,
Time holds the heart's key,
key to ev - 'ry - thing is
love,
Love makes the heart flow'r,
Flow'rs in - to a deep de - sire.
Pas - sion in the
hearts fire.
Pas - sion and de - sire.

Riverdance

Composed by Bill Whelan · Lyrics by Bill Whelan

Copyright © 1994 McGuinness/Whelan Music Publishing Ltd & RTÉ Music Ltd.
International copyright secured. All Rights Reserved.
Boosey & Hawkes Music Publishers Ltd sole agents.

I am pul - sing the blood in your veins.
Feel the mag - ic and power of sur - ren - der to life.
mp
1.
2.
ritard.
Lively
Am
mf
Em7
Asus2

E7sus4
Asus2
E7sus4
Fadd9
Gsus4
Fadd9
Gsus4
Asus2
Em7
Asus2

The Countess Cathleen

Composed by Bill Whelan

Copyright © 1994 McGuinness/Whelan Music Publishing Ltd. International copyright secured. All Rights Reserved.
Boosey & Hawkes Music Publishers Ltd sole agents.

G/B D/F♯ C/E G/D C G/B Am G
D5
1. Em D/F♯
2. Em D/F♯
D A/D G/D D
f
Am7 G/B D A/D G/D
D Am7 G/B Fmaj7

Segue to "Women of the Sidhe"

Women of the Sidhe

Composed by Bill Whelan

Copyright © 1994 McGuinness/Whelan Music Publishing Ltd. International copyright secured. All Rights Reserved.
Boosey & Hawkes Music Publishers Ltd sole agents.

E5
Asus4
E5
D5
1.
2.
E5
Asus4
E5
Asus4
ff
E5
Asus4
E5
fff

Shivna

Composed by Bill Whelan · Lyrics by Anonymous

Copyright © 1994 McGuinness/Whelan Music Publishing Ltd. International copyright secured. All Rights Reserved.
Boosey & Hawkes Music Publishers Ltd sole agents.

1.
2.
mf
cresc.
f
ff

The Harvest

Composed by Bill Whelan

Copyright © 1994 McGuinness/Whelan Music Publishing Ltd. International copyright secured. All Rights Reserved.
Boosey & Hawkes Music Publishers Ltd sole agents.

A
D/A
Am7
G/A
A
D/A
A7
D/A
A7
Bm
Em
D/F♯
G
Em
A
D
Em
A7
D
ff

American Wake

Composed by Bill Whelan

Copyright © 1994 McGuinness/Whelan Music Publishing Ltd. International copyright secured. All Rights Reserved.
Boosey & Hawkes Music Publishers Ltd sole agents.

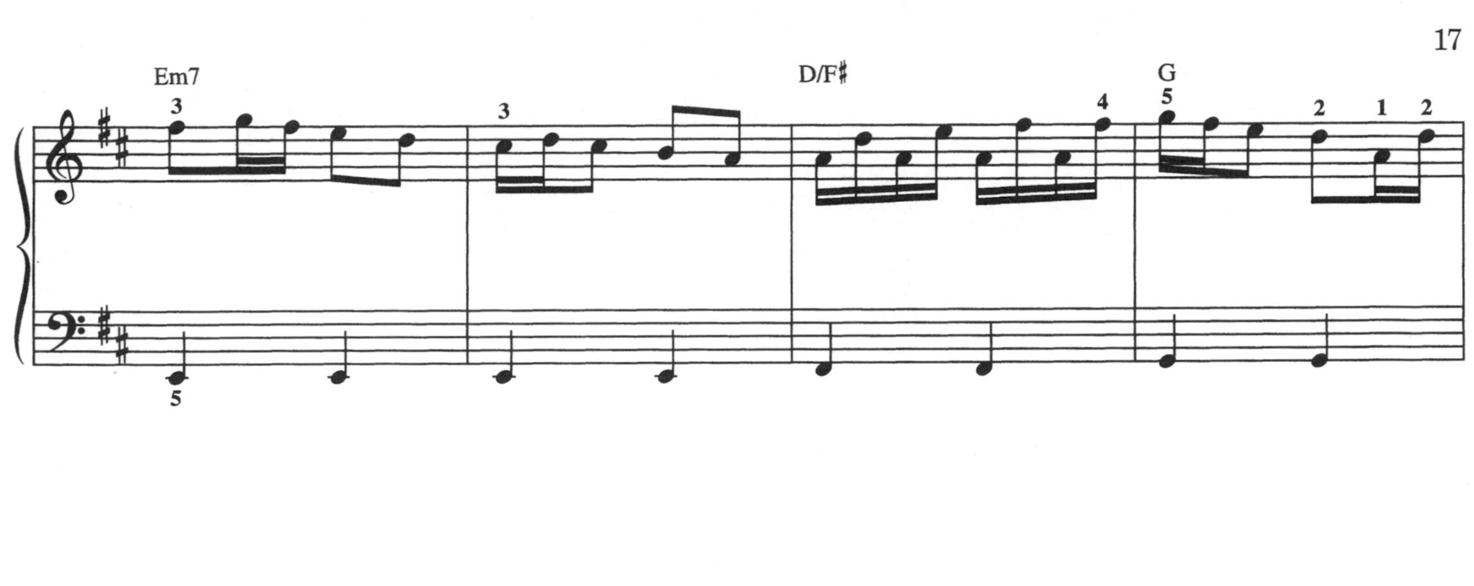
Em7
D/F♯
G

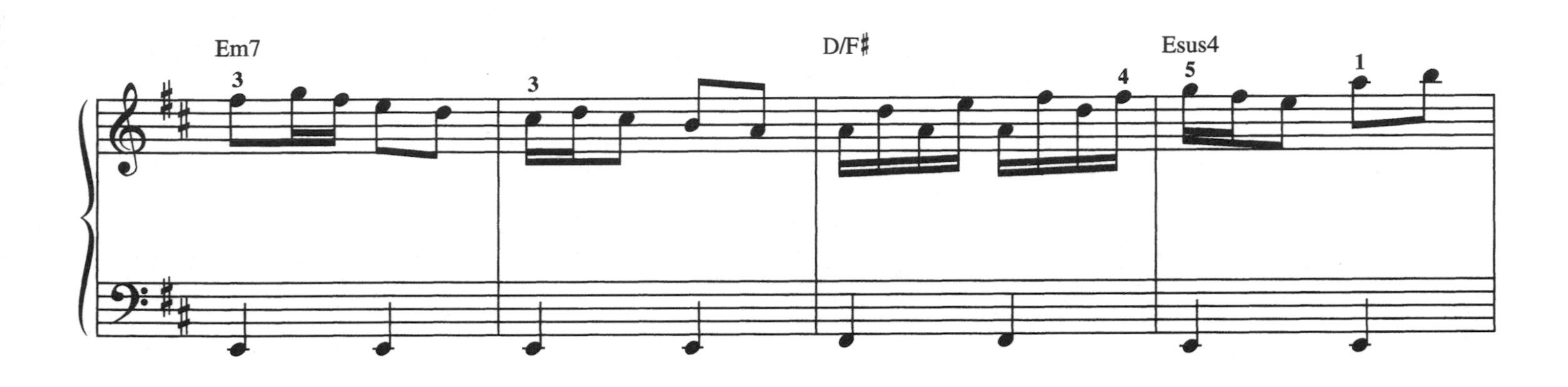
Em7
D/F♯
Esus4

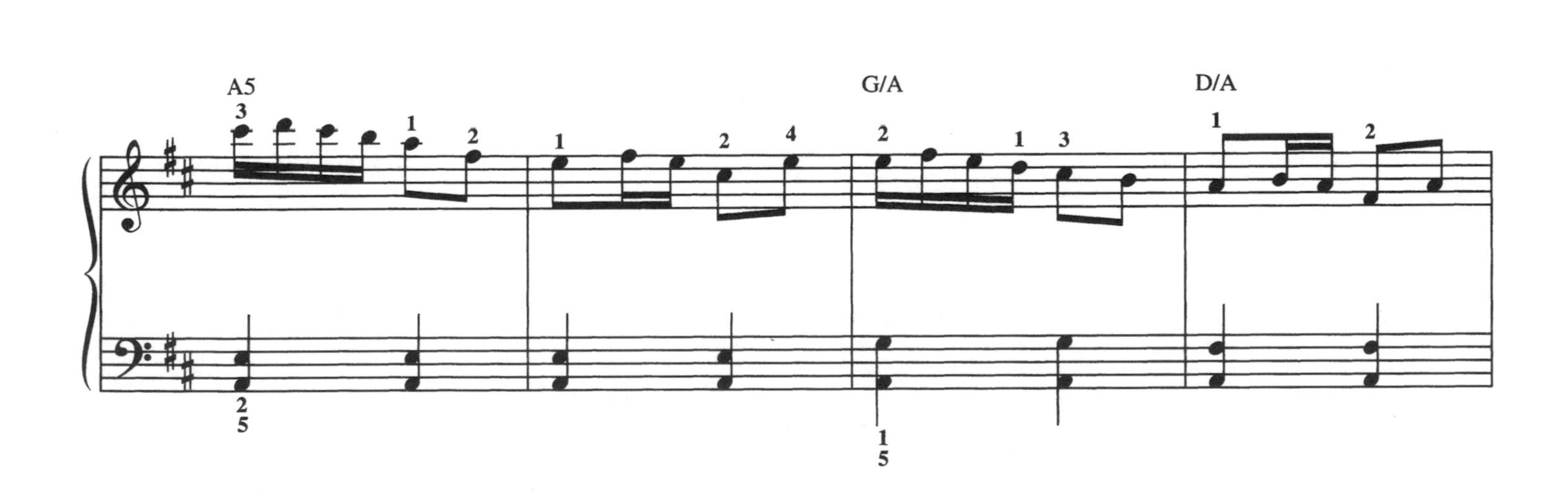
A5
G/A
D/A

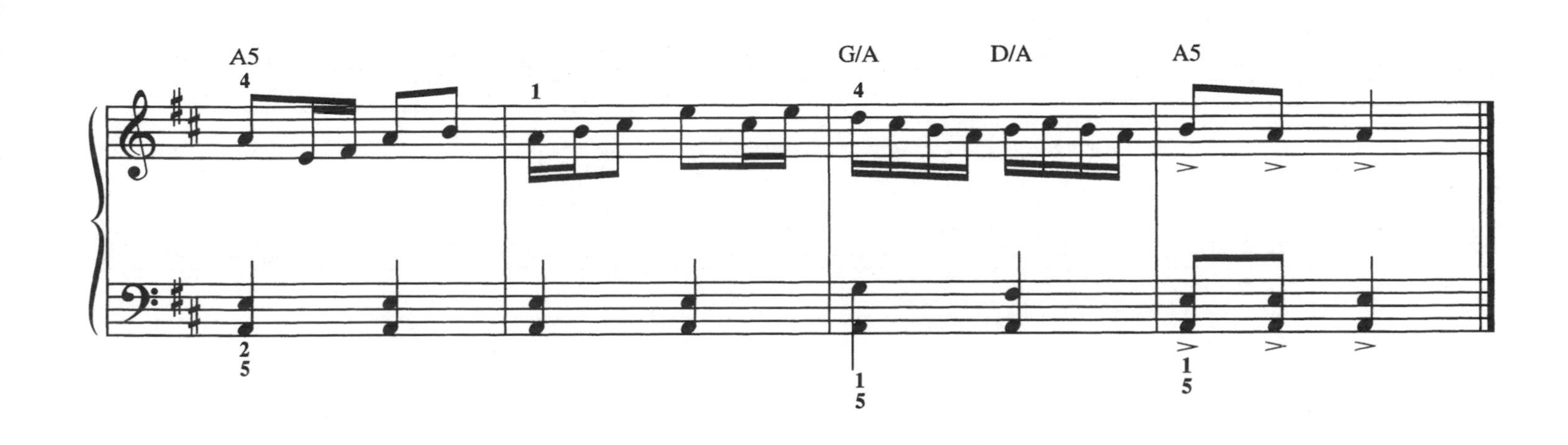
A5
G/A
D/A
A5

Lift the Wings

Composed by Bill Whelan · Lyrics by Bill Whelan

Copyright © 1994 McGuinness/Whelan Music Publishing Ltd. International copyright secured. All Rights Reserved.
Boosey & Hawkes Music Publishers Ltd sole agents.

F F/A B♭ C
fill the sail that breaks the line to home. But when I'm
Dm Am B♭ F Gm F C Gm/B♭
miles and miles a - part from you, I'm be -
F/C B♭/C
side you when I think of you, a stóir -
to next strain
F Gm7
in, a ghrá.
Fine
F/C B♭/C
in. And I'm with you as I dream of you, a stóir - in. And this

F/C
B♭/C
F
song will bring me near to you, a
stóir - in, a
ghrá.
ritard. e dim.
mp
Verse
C5
Am
F
mp
2. How can a tree stand
tall if a rain won't
Melody
B♭
F5add9
E♭
F5add9
fall to wash its
branch - es down? And
C5
Am
F
how can the heart sur - vive,
can it stay a -
B♭
F5add9
E♭
C/E
D.S. al Fine
live if its love's de -
nied for long?

Home and the Heartland

Composed by Bill Whelan · Lyrics by Bill Whelan

Copyright © 1994 McGuinness/Whelan Music Publishing Ltd. International copyright secured. All Rights Reserved.
Boosey & Hawkes Music Publishers Ltd sole agents.

C6
G/B
C6
one sweet
place, home and the
heart - land.
ris - ing
from home and the
heart - land.
D7sus4
G
A/G
Sing
out your
mf
D/F♯
D
Em7
D/F♯
G
songs and
ring out your
sto -
A/G
Bsus4
ries and
rhymes.
G
A/G
D/F♯
Weave
from your
dreams those

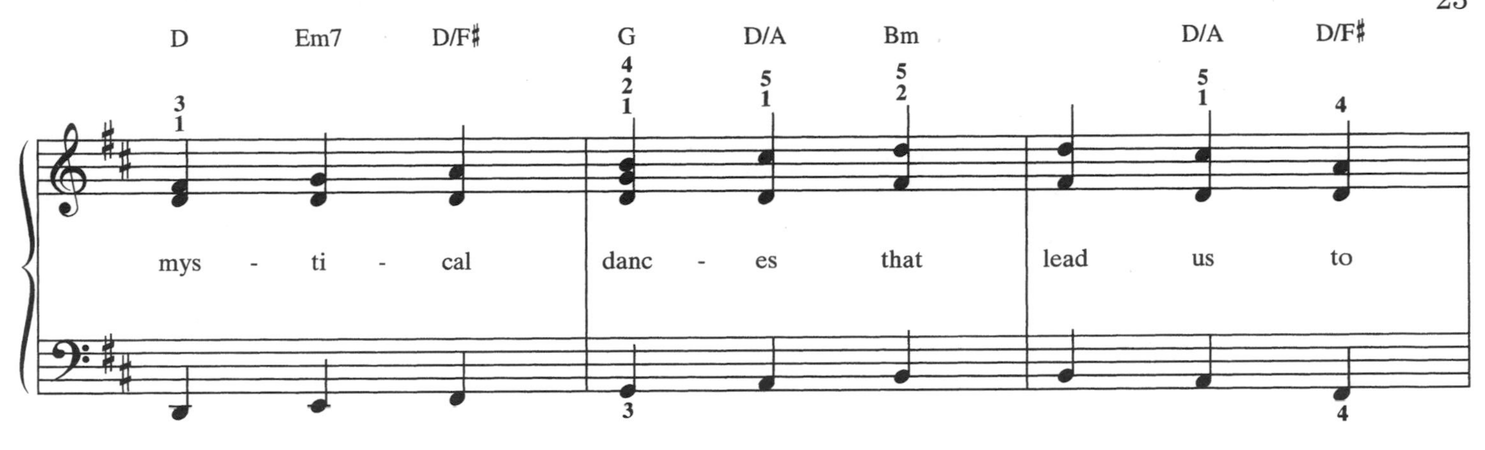
D Em7 D/F♯ G D/A Bm D/A D/F♯
mys - ti - cal danc - es that lead us to

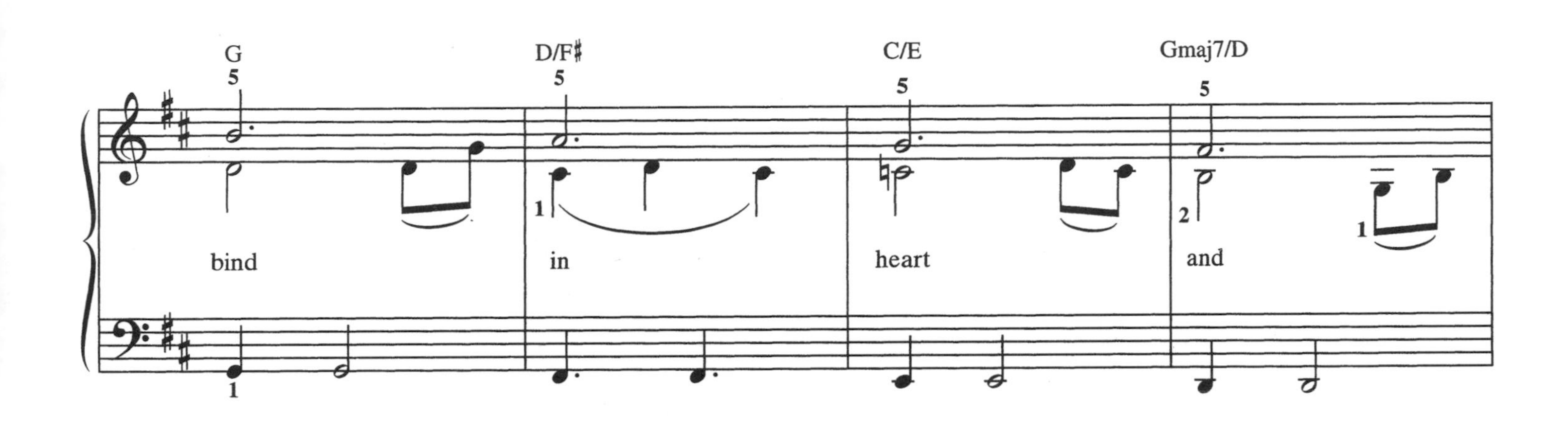
G D/F♯ C/E Gmaj7/D
bind in heart and

C6/9 D7sus4
1.
mind.
2. As we

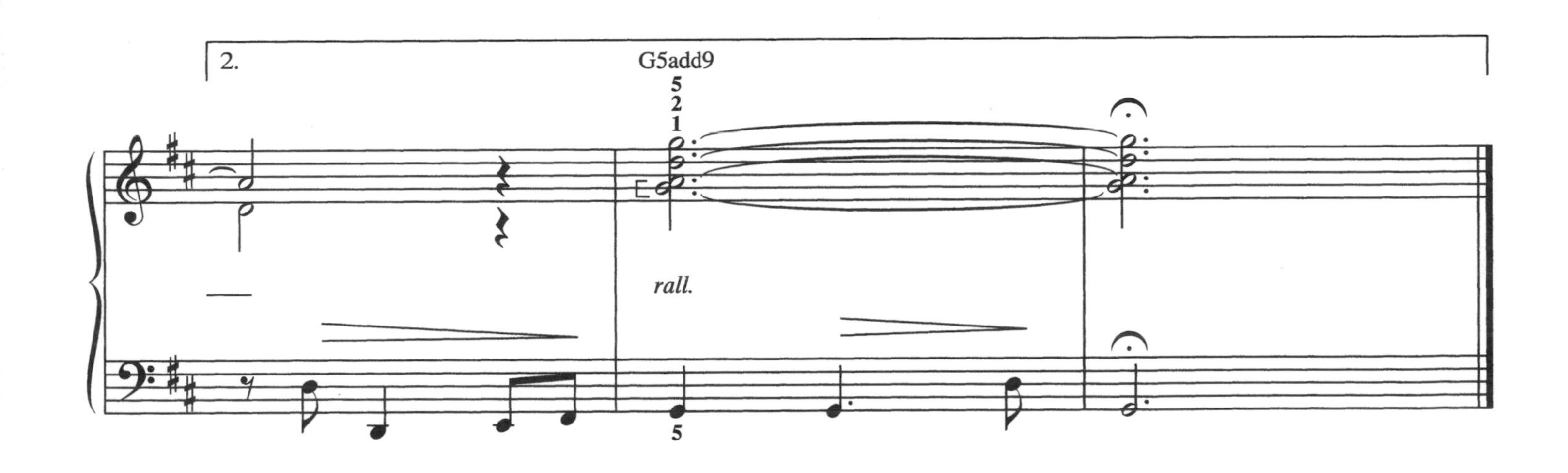
2.
G5add9
rall.

Heal Their Hearts

Composed by Bill Whelan · Lyrics by Bill Whelan

Copyright © 1994 McGuinness/Whelan Music Publishing Ltd. International copyright secured. All Rights Reserved.
Boosey & Hawkes Music Publishers Ltd sole agents.

D/A Gm/B♭ A7/C♯ Dm7 C/G G C
spir - it ris - es when a - wok - en.
on to reach a new ho - ri - zon.
Yes, they may be poor in
F C7 F C F C7 F
birth, but yes, how great each one is worth.
B♭ E/B F/C B♭ F/A F♯°7
Heal their hearts, feed their souls, Their
Gm B♭/F Cm/E♭ A/C♯ F/C C7 1. F
lives can be gold - en if your love en - folds.
Bm B7sus4 E/B G/B 2. F
2. In their folds.

Macedonian Morning

Composed by Bill Whelan

Copyright © 1994 McGuinness/Whelan Music Publishing Ltd. International copyright secured. All Rights Reserved.
Boosey & Hawkes Music Publishers Ltd sole agents.

Dm7
E/D
Gm add9
Fmaj7/A
B♭maj9

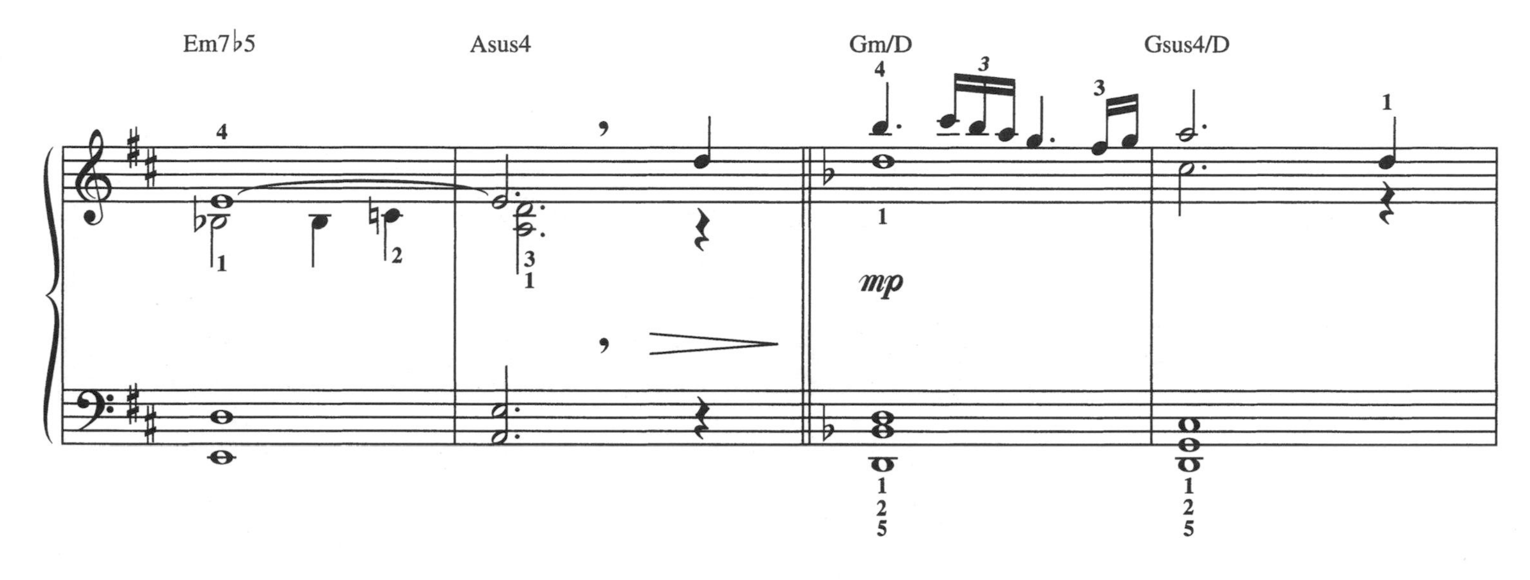
Em7♭5
Asus4
Gm/D
Gsus4/D
mp

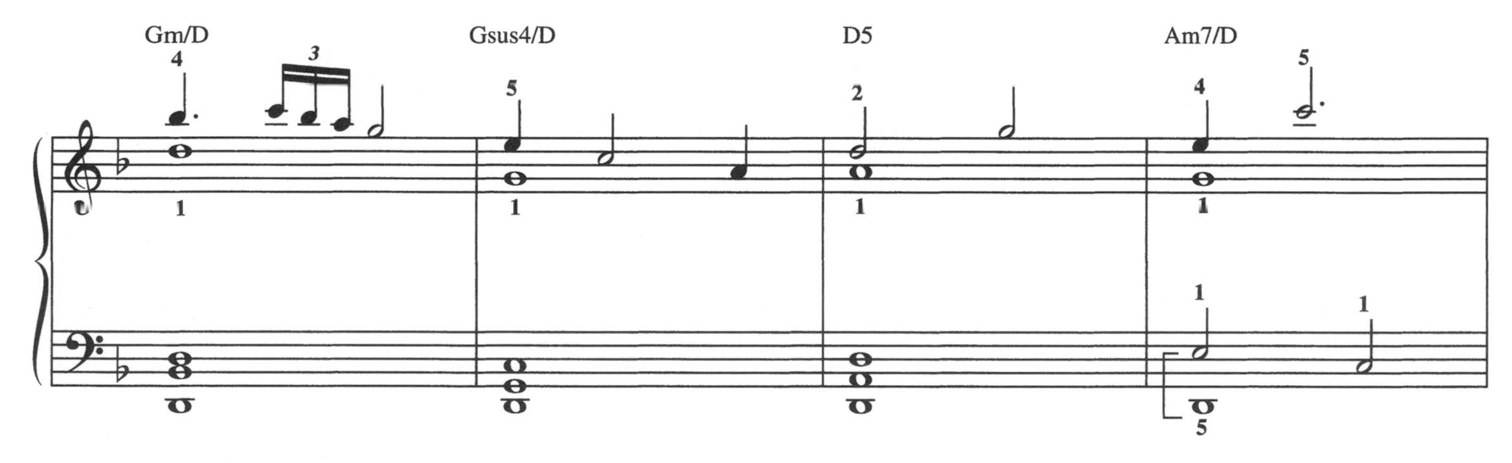
Gm/D
Gsus4/D
D5
Am7/D

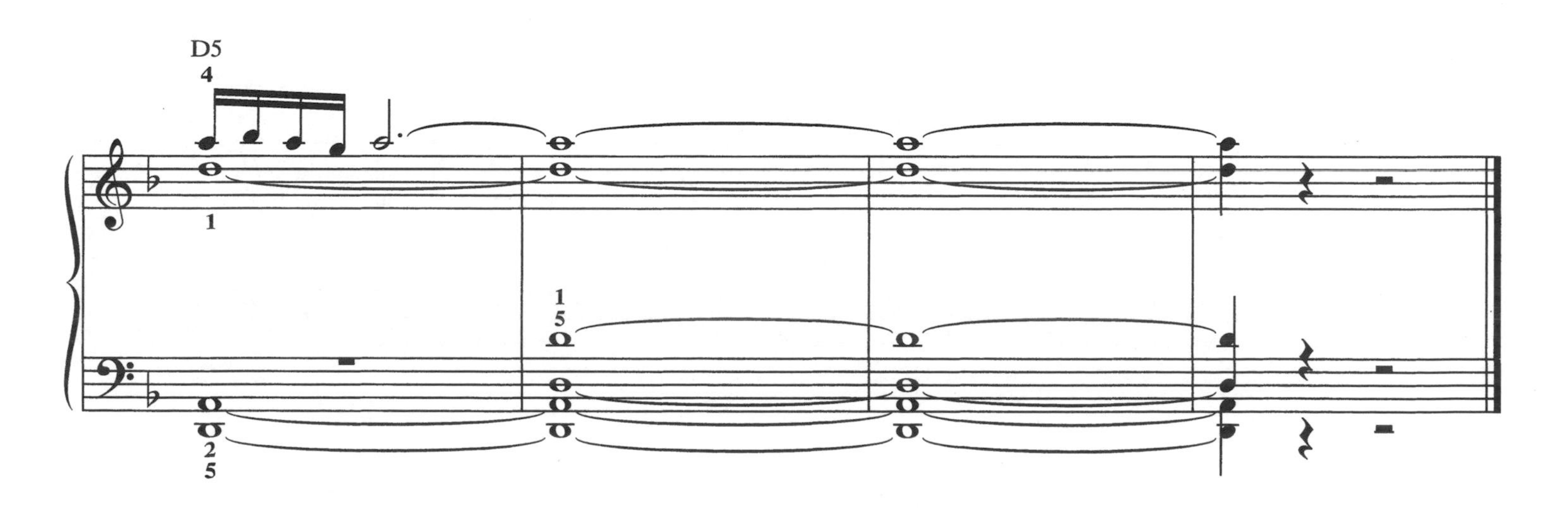
D5

Oscail An Doras

Composed by Bill Whelan · Lyrics by Anonymous

Copyright © 1994 McGuinness/Whelan Music Publishing Ltd. International copyright secured. All Rights Reserved.
Boosey & Hawkes Music Publishers Ltd sole agents.